Irish Songs

First published in 2019 by
Appletree Press Ltd
Roycroft House
164 Malone Road
Belfast BT9 5LL

Tel: +44 (0) 28 90 24 30 74
Fax: +44 (0) 28 90 24 67 56
E-mail: reception@appletree.ie
Web: www.appletree.ie

A member of Publishing Ireland

Copyright © Appletree Press, 2008, 2019
Typeset by Timothy Murphy

A catalogue record for this book is available from the British Library.

Irish Songs

ISBN: 978 1 84758 175 4

Desk and Marketing Editor: Jean Brown
Copy-editor: Jim Black
Designer: Stuart Wilkinson
Production Manager: Paul McAvoy

9 8 7 6 5 4 3 2 1

AP3819

Irish Songs

Traditional Songs

Irish tin whistle and bodhran

Contents

Lakes of Killarney

Danny Boy

Oh Dan - ny Boy, the pipes the pipes are call - ing_____ from

glen to glen_____ and down the moun - tain side_____ The sum - mer's

gone and all the ros - es fall - ing 'tis you, 'tis you, must

go and I must bide. But come ye back when sum - mer's in the

mea - dow, or when the val - ley's hushed and white with snow.

'Tis I'll be there in sun - shine or in sha - dow

Oh Dan - ny Boy, Oh Dan - ny Boy I love you so.

And when ye come and all the flowers are dying,
If I am dead, as dead I well may be,
You'll come and find the place where I am lying,
And kneel and say an Ave there for me.
And I shall hear, tho' soft you tread above me,
And all my grave will warmer, sweeter be,
If you will bend and tell me that you love me,
Then I shall sleep in peace until you come to me.

Monasterboice, Co. Louth

The Lark in the Morning

Chorus: The lark in the mor - ning_ she ri - ses from her nest_ She goes

off _ ev - ery mor - ning_ with the dew all on _ her breast_ And

like the jol - ly plough boy she whist - les and she sings_ She goes

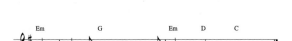

home_ ev - ery ev - en - ing with the dew all on her wings_

Oh, Roger the ploughboy, he is a dashing blade,
He goes whistling and sighing over yonder green glade,
He met with pretty Susan, she's handsome I declare,
She is far more enticing than the birds in the air.

Chorus

One evening coming home from the rakes of the town,
The meadows being all green and the grass it being cut down,
If I should chance to tumble all in the new mown hay,
Oh, it's kiss me now or never, love, this bonny lass did say.

Chorus

When twenty long weeks they were over and were past,
Her mammy chanced to notice she'd thickened round the waist,
It was the handsome ploughboy the maiden she did say,
For he caused me for to tumble all in the new-mown hay.

Chorus

Here's a health to young ploughboys, wherever you may be,
That likes to have a bonny lass a-sitting on his knee
With a jug of good strong porter, you'll whistle and you'll sing,
For a ploughboy is as happy as a prince or a king.

Chorus

The Curragh of Kildare

The win - ter it is past and the sum-mer's come at last. The

birds they are sing-ing in __ the trees_____ Their lit - tle hearts are
straight I will re -

glad, but__ mine is ve - ry sad For my true love is
pair to the Cur - ragh of Kil - dare For it's there I'll find

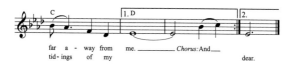

far a - way from me. _____ *Chorus:* And__
tid - ings of my dear.

The rose upon the briar by the water running clear
Brings joy to the linnet and the deer
Their little hearts are blessed, but mine knows no rest
For my true love is absent from me.

Chorus

A livery I'll wear and I'll comb back my hair
And in velvet so green I will appear
And straight I will repair to the Curragh of Kildare
For it's there I'll find tidings of my dear.

Chorus

O you that are in love, and cannot it remove
I pity the pain you do endure,
For experience lets me know that your hearts are full of woe
A woe that no mortal can cure.

Chorus

Irish Jockey

The Galway Races

As   I rode down to   Gal-way town to   seek for re-cre-
There were   pas-sen-gers from Lim-er-ick and more from Tipp-er-

a-tion on   the   sev-en-teenth of Au-gust me   mind being el-e-
ar-y, Boys from Con-nem-ar-a_____ and a   flair of mar-ried

va-ted. There were   mul-ti-tudes as-sem-bled with their
la-dies, peo-ple from Cork ci-ty   who were loy-al

tick-ets at   the   sta-tion.___ Me   eyes be-gan to
true___ and faith-ful_____ Brought home the Fe-nian

daz – zle and I'm going to see the Rac – es. With your
pri – son – ers, from dying in fo – reign na – tions. With your

whack – fa – the da for the di – dd – ly di – ddle a_____
whack – fa – the da for the di – dd – ly di – ddle a_____

Connemara pony, Co. Galway

It's there you'll see the pipers
And the fiddlers competing,
The nimble-footed dancers,
A-tripping over the daisies.
There were others crying, cigars and likes,
And bills for all the races,
With the colours of the jockeys
And the prices and horses' ages.
With your whack-fa-the-da,
For the diddly-diddle-a.

It's there you'll see the jockeys,
And they're mounted out so stately,
The pink, the blue, the orange and green,
The emblem of our Nation.
When the bell was rung for starting,
All the horses seemed impatient,
I thought they never stood on ground,
Their speed was so amazing.
With your whack-fa-the-da,
For the diddly-diddle-a.

There was half a million people there,
From all denominations,
The Catholic, the Protestant,
The Jew and Presbyterian.
There was yet no animosity,
No matter what persuasion,
But sportsman hospitality
And induce fresh acquaintance.
With your whack-fa-the-da,
For the diddly-diddle-a.

Believe Me, If All Those Endearing Young Charms

Be - lieve me, if all those en - dear-ing young charms which I

gaze on so fond-ly to - day____ Were to change by to-mor-row, and

fleet in my arms, Like fai-ry gifts fad-ing a - way.____ Thou would'st

still be a-dor'd, as this mo-ment thou art, Let thy love-li-ness fade as it

will, _____ and a - round the dear ru - in each

wish of my heart would en - twine it - self ver - dant-ly still. _____

It is not while beauty and youth are thine own,
And thy cheeks unprofan'd by a tear,
That the fervour and faith of a soul can be known,
To which time will but make thee more dear.
No, the heart that has truly lov'd, never forgets,
But as truly loves on to the close,
As the sunflower turns to her god, when he sets,
The same look which she turn'd when he rose.

Statue of Annie Moore and her two brothers, the first Irish emigrants to pass through Ellis Island, New York before entering the United States

The Shores of Amerikay

I'm bid-ding fa-re-well to the land of my youth and the home I

love so well.____ And the moun-tains so grand round my own na-tive

land, I'm bid-ding them all____ fare-well.____ With an ach-ing

hea-rt I'll bid them a-dieu for to-mor-row I'll sail far a-way,____

Irish Songs

_____ o'er the ra - ging_____ foam for to se - ek a

home on the shores of A - mer - i - kay._____

'Tears like rain will blind' – Co. Donegal

It's not for the want of employment I'm going,
It's not for the love of fame,
That fortune bright, may shine over me
And give me a glorious name.
It's not for the want of employment I'm going
O'er the weary and stormy sea,
But to seek a home for my own true love,
On the shores of Amerikay.

And when I am bidding my last farewell
The tears like rain will blind,
To think of my friends in my own native land,
And the home I'm leaving behind.
But if I'm to die in a foreign land
And be buried so far far away
No fond mother's tears will be shed o'er my grave,
On the shores of Amerikay.

The Black Velvet Band

Chorus: Her eyes they shone like dia-monds, __ I

thought her the Queen of the land___ And her

hair hung o-ver her shoul – ders Tied

up with a black vel-vet band.___

As I went walking down Broadway,
Not intending to stay very long,
I met with a frolicsome damsel,
As she came a-tripping along,
She was both fair and handsome,
Her neck it was white as a swan,
And her hair hung over her shoulder,
Tied up with a black velvet band.

Chorus

I took a stroll with this pretty fair maid
When a gentleman passed us by,
I knew she had the taking of him
By the look in her roguish black eye.
A gold watch she took from his pocket
And put it right into my hand
On the very first day that I met her,
Bad luck to the black velvet band.

Chorus

Before judge and jury next morning
Both of us had to appear.
The judge he said to me, 'Young man,
Your case is proven clear,'
Seven long years' transportation,
Right on down to Van Diemen's Land
Far away from my friends and relations
Betrayed by the black velvet band.

Chorus

Carrickfergus Castle and Harbour

Carrickfergus

I wish I was _____ in Car-rick - fer - gus _____ On-ly for

nights _____ in Ball-y - gran _____ I would swim o - ver _____

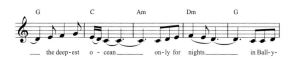

_____ the deep-est o - cean _____ on-ly for nights _____ in Ball-y-

gran _____ But the sea is wide _____ and I can-not swim o - ver _____

_____ And neith - er have_ I_____ the wings to fly_____ I wish I

could find_____ a hand - some boat - man_____

_____ To ferry me o - ver____ to my love and die.

My boyhood days bring back sad reflections
Of happy hours I spent long ago,
Of boyhood friends and my own relations
Are all passed on now, like drifting snow;
But I'll spend my days an endless rover,
Soft is the grass I walk, my bed is free;
Ah, to be back in Carrickfergus
On that long road, down to the sea.

But in Kilkenny it is reported
There are marble stones there, as black as ink,
With gold and silver I would support her
But I'll sing no more till I get a drink.
I'm drunk today and I'm seldom sober,
A handsome rover from town to town,
Ah, but I'm sick now and my days are numbered
So come all you young men and lay me down.

'He rapped at her bedroom window'

I'm A Rover

I'm a ro - ver, sel-dom so - ber, I'm a ro - ver of high de-

gree_____ It's when I'm drink - ing I'm al - ways think - ing, How to

gain my_ love's com - pa - ny. I'm a - ny.

Though the night be as dark as dungeon,
Not a star to be seen above
I will be guided without a stumble
Into the arms of my own true love.

'The cocks were crowing...'

He stepped up to her bedroom window;
Kneeling gently upon a stone
He rapped at her bedroom window:
'Darling dear, do you lie alone.

'It's only me your own true lover;
Open the door and let me in;
For I have come on a long journey,
And I'm near drenched unto the skin.'

She opened the door with the greatest pleasure,
She opened the door and she let him in;
They both took hands and embraced each other;
Until the morning they lay as one.

The cocks were crowing, the birds were singing,
The burns they ran free about the brae;
'Remember lass I'm a ploughman's laddie,
And the farmer I must obey.

'Now my love I must go and leave thee;
And though the hills they are high above,
I will climb them with greater pleasure,
Since I've been in your arms my love.'

'Yon fair mountains' – Wicklow Mountains

Slieve Gallion Braes

Unaccompanied

As I went a - walk - ing ___ one ___ morn - ing in May, To

view yon fair moun - tains and val - leys so gay, I was think - ing on those

flow - ers, ___ all ___ go - ing to ___ de - cay, That ___

bloom - a - round yon ___ bon - ny, bon - ny, Slieve Gal - lion Braes.

'I roamed through the glens' – Ring of Kerry

It's oft I did ramble with
My dog and my gun,
I roamed through the glens
For joy and for fun,
But those days are now all over and
I can no longer stay,
So farewell unto ye, bonny,
Bonny Slieve Gallion braes.

How oft of an evening
And the sun in the west,
I roved hand in hand
With the one I loved best:
But the hopes of youth are vanished
And now I'm far away,
So farewell unto ye, bonny,
Bonny Slieve Gallion braes.

O! It was not for the want
Of employment at home,
That caused the young sons
Of old Ireland to roam,
But the rents are getting higher and
I can no longer stay,
So farewell unto ye, bonny,
Bonny Slieve Gallion braes.

Irish Pub Window

Whiskey in the Jar

Capo 2nd

As I was goi - ing o - ver the far famed Ker - ry moun - tains, I
He count - ed out his mon - ey, it made a pret - ty pen - ny, I

met with Cap - tain Far - rell and his mon - ey he was count - ing____ I
put it in my pock - et and I gave it to my Jen - ny,____ She

first pro - duced my pis - tol and then put out my rap - ier Say - ing
sigh'd and she swore___ she nev - er would be - tray me But the

stand and de - liv - er for you are the bold de - ceiv - er With my
devil take the wo - men for they nev - er can be ea - sy With my

I went to my chamber all for to take a slumber,
I dreamt of gold and jewels and sure it was no wonder,
But Jenny drew my charges
And she filled them up with water,
And she sent for Captain Farrell,
To be ready for the slaughter.

Chorus

And 'twas early in the morning before I rose to travel,
Up comes a band of footmen and likewise Captain Farrell;
I then produced my pistol,
For she stole away my rapier
But I couldn't shoot the water so
A prisoner I was taken.

Chorus

And if anyone can aid me, 'tis my brother in the army,
If I could learn his station in Cork or in Killarney.
And if he'd come and join me
We'd go roving in Kilkenny,
I'll engage he'd treat me fairer
Than my darling sporting Jenny.

Chorus

There's some take delight in the hurling and the bowling,
Others take delight in the carriages a-rolling;
But I take delight
In the juice of the barley,
And courting pretty women when
The sun is rising early.

Chorus

Loughshore in Co. Galway

The West's Awake

When all be-side a vi-gil keep, The West's a-sleep, the

West's a-sleep. A - las, and well may E - rin weep that

Con-nacht lies in slum-ber deep, There lake and plain smile

fair and free, 'Mid rocks their guar-dian chiv - al - ry, Sing

oh! let man learn li-ber-ty, from crash-ing wind and lash-ing sea!

That chainless wave and lovely land
Freedom and nationhood demand
Be sure the great God never planned,
For slumb'ring slaves a home so grand,
And long a proud and haughty race
Honour'd and sentinell'd the place
Sing, oh! not e'en their sons' disgrace,
Can quite destroy their glory's trace.

For often in O'Connor's van
To triumph dashed each Connacht clan,
And fleet as deer the Normans ran
Through Curlieu's Pass and Ardrahan;
And later times saw deeds as brave,
And glory guards Clanricarde's grave;
Sing oh! They died their land to save,
At Aughrim's slopes and Shannon's wave.

And if, when all a vigil keep,
The West's asleep, the West's asleep,
Alas! and may well Erin weep,
That Connacht lies in slumber deep;
But hark! a voice like thunder spake;
The West's awake! The West's awake!
Sing oh, hurrah! Let England quake!
We'll watch 'til death for Erin's sake.

'Oh list' to the lay of a poor Irish harper'

The Bard of Armagh

Oh list' to the lay of a poor Ir-ish har-per and scorn not the

string of his old with-ered hands, but re-mem-ber those fin-gers they

once could move shar-per to raise up the strains of his dear na-tive land.

It was long before the shamrock, dear isle's lovely emblem,
Was crushed in its beauty by the Saxon's lion paw;
And all the pretty colleens around me would gather,
Call me their bold Phelim Brady, the Bard of Armagh.

'The shamrock, dear isle's lovely emblem'

How I love to muse on the days of my boyhood,
Though four score and three years have fled by them;
It's king's sweet reflection that every young joy,
For the merry-hearted boys make the best of old men.

At a fair or a wake I would twist my shillelah,
And trip through a dance with my brogues tied with straw;
There all the pretty maidens around me gather,
Call me their bold Phelim Brady, the Bard of Armagh.

In truth I have wandered this wide world over,
Yet Ireland's my home and a dwelling for me;
And oh, let the turf that my old bones shall cover,
Be cut from the land that is trod by the free.

And when Sergeant Death in his cold arms doth embrace,
And lull me to sleep with old Erin-go-bragh,
By the side of my Kathleen, my dear pride, oh, place me,
Then forget Phelim Brady, the Bard of Armagh.

My Singing Bird

I have seen the lark so-ar high at morn to___ sing__ up__ in the

blue, I have heard the black - bird___ pipe its song, the___

thrush and the lin - net too. But__ none of them can sing so sweet, my

sing - ing bird__ as___ you. Ah___

My — sing - ing — bird as you.

If I could lure my singing bird from its own cosy nest,
If I could lure my singing bird I would warm it on my breast
And on my heart my singing bird would sing itself to rest,
Ah–, would sing itself to rest.

'I have heard the blackbird pipe its song'

Follow Me Up to Carlow

Lift, Mac Cath-air Óg, your face, Brood-ing o'er the old dis-grace, That
Grey said vic-to - ry was sure, Soon the fire-brand he'd se - cure, Un-

Black Fitz-wil-liam stormed your place And drove you to the fern____
-til he met at Glen-ma-lure, with Feagh Mac Hugh O' Byrne!____

Chorus:
Curse and swear Lord Kil-dare, Feagh will do what Feagh will dare,

Now Fitz-wil - liam have a care, Fal - len is ___ your star low.

52

Up with hal-berd out with sword, On we'll go for by the Lord—

Feagh Mac Hugh has giv-en the word, 'Fol-low me up to Car - low.'

See the swords of Glen Imail
Flashing o'er the English Pale,
See the children of the Gael
Beneath O'Byrne's banners.
Rooster of a fighting stock,
Would you let a Saxon cock,
Crow out upon an Irish rock;
Fly up and teach him manners.

Chorus

From Tassagart to Clonmore
Flows a stream of Saxon gore,
Och! Great was Ruari Óg O'More
At sending loons to Hades.
White is sick and Lane is fled –
Now for black Fitzwilliam's head –
We'll send it over dripping red
To Liza and her ladies.

Chorus

Blarney Castle, Co. Cork

Clare's Dragoons

When on Ram-ill-ies' blood-y field the baf-fled French were

forced to yield, The vic-tor Sax-on__ back-ward reel'd Be -

fore the charge of Clare's men. The flags we con-quer'd

in that fray look lone in Y-pres' choir. Then say; We'll

win them com-pan - y to-day or_ brave-ly die like

Clare's men. *Chorus:* Vi - ve là! For Ire-land's wrong,

Vi - ve là! For Ire-land's right, And vi - ve là in__

bat - tle throng for a Span-ish steed and sa - bre.

Another Clare is here to lead,
The worthy son of such a breed,
The French expect some famous deed
When Clare leads on his warriors.
Our Colonel comes from Brian's race,
His wounds are in his breast and face,
The gap of danger's still his place,
The foremost of his squadron.

Chorus

Oh, comrades, think how Ireland pines
For exiled lords and rifled shrines,
Her dearest hope the ordered lines
And bursting charge of Clare's men.
Then fling your green flag to the sky,
Be Limerick your battle cry,
And charge 'til blood floats fetlock high
Around the track of Clare's men.

Chorus

Pretty Susan, the Pride of Kildare

When from sea first I land-ed with rov-ing in mind, Un-daunt-ed I ram-bled my

true love to find, I met pret-ty Su-san with cheeks like a

rose,____ And her bo-som more fair than the li-ly that grows.____

Her keen eyes did glitter like
Bright stars by night,
And the robes she was wearing
Were costly and white,
Her bare neck was shaded
With her long raven hair,
And they call her pretty Susan,
The Pride of Kildare.

Sometimes I am jovial,
Sometimes I am sad,
Since my love she is courted
By some other lad,
But since we're at a distance,
No more I'll despair,
So my blessings on Susan,
The Pride of Kildare.

Ha' Penny Bridge over River Liffey, Dublin

The Little Beggerman

I am a lit - tle beg-gar-man a beg-ging I have been Aye for

three score and ten__ in this lit - tle isle of green And up__ to the Lif - fey__

down to Tess-a-gue And I'm known by the name of the Bold John-ny Dhu. Of

all the trades a'-go - in'__ a - beg-ging is the best For__

61

when a man is tired___ He can sit him down and rest. He

begs___ for his din-ner he has noth-ing else to do, On - ly

cut a-round the cor-ner with his old rin-ga-do -l   old rin-ga-do.

I slept last night in a barn at Curraghbawn,
A wet night came on and I skipped through the door,
Holes in my shoes and my toes peeping through,
Singin' skiddy-me-re-doodlum, for old Johnny Dhu.
I must be gettin' home for it's gettin' late at night,
The fire's all raked and there isn't any light.
An' now you've heard me story of the old ringadoo,
It's good night and God bless you from ould Johnny Dhu.

'The fire's all raked and there isn't any light'

Peace and quiet in an Irish Snug

The Wild Rover

I've been a wild rov - er for ma - ny's a year_____ And I've

spent all my mon - ey on whis - key and beer_____ And now I'm re -

turn - ing with gold in great store_____ And I nev - er will play the wild

rov - er no more. And it's no! nay! nev - er!

no nay nev-er no more,_____ And I'll play_____

___ the wild rov-er_____ no nev-er_____ no more.

'I asked her for credit, she answered me nay.'

I went into an alehouse I used to frequent,
And I told the landlady my money was spent.
I asked her for credit, she answered me nay,
Saying custom like yours I can have any day.

Chorus

I took from my pocket ten sovereigns bright,
And the landlady's eyes opened wide with delight,
She said I have whiskeys and wines of the best,
And the words that I told you were only in jest.

Chorus

I'll go home to my parents, confess what I've done
And I'll ask them to pardon their prodigal son.
And when they have kissed me as oft-times before,
I never will play the wild rover no more.

Chorus

I will Walk with My Love

I once loved a boy and a bold I-rish boy Who would

come and would go at my re-quest, And this bold I-rish boy was my

pride and my joy And I built him a bower in my breast.

But this girl who has ta-ken my bon-ny, bon-ny boy Let her

make of him all that she can, And whe-ther he loves me or

loves me not, I will walk with my love now and then.

Croagh Patrick, Co. Mayo

'Down beside the kitchen fire'

The Jolly Beggar

It's of a jol - ly beg - gar - man came trip - ping o'er the
far - mer's daugh - ter she came down and viewed him cheek and

plain_____ He came un - to a farm - er's door a lodg - ing for to
chin_____ She said he is a hand - some man, I pray you take him

gain____ The go no more a - rov - ing a - rov - ing in the
in____ *Chorus:* We'll

night ____ We'll go no more a - rov - ing let the

moon__ shine so bright__ We'll go no more a - rov - ing.

He would not lie within the barn
Nor yet within the byre,
But he would in the corner lie,
Down by the kitchen fire,
And when the beggar's bed was made
Of good clean sheets and hay,
Down beside the kitchen fire
The jolly beggar lay.

Chorus

The farmer's daughter she came down
To bolt the kitchen door,
And there she saw the beggar
Standing naked on the floor.
He took the daughter in his arms
And to the bed he ran
Kind sir, she says, be easy now,
You'll waken our good man.

Chorus

Now you are no beggar,
You are some gentleman,
For you have stole my maidenhead
And I am quite undone.
I am no lord, I am no squire,
Of beggars I be one,
And beggars they be robbers all,
So you are quite undone.

Chorus

She took the bed in both her hands
And threw it at the wall,
Saying, go you with the beggarman,
My maidenhead and all.
We'll go no more a-roving,
A-roving in the night,
We'll go no more a-roving,
Let the moon shine so bright,
We'll go no more a-roving.

Irish Wild Rose – 'Last Rose of the Summer'

The Last Rose of Summer

'Tis the last rose of__ sum-mer Left__bloom-ing__a - lone All her

love-ly com - pan-ions Are__ fa - ded__ and__ gone! No__ flow'r of__ her__

kin - dred, No__ rose-bud__ is__ nigh,_____ To re-

flect back her__ blu - shes, Or__ give sigh__ for__ sigh.

I'll not leave thee, thou lone one,
To pine on the stem,
Since the lovely are sleeping,
Go, sleep thou with them;
Thus kindly I scatter
Thy leaves o'er the bed
Where thy mates of the garden
Lie scentless and dead.

So soon may I follow,
When friendships decay,
And from Love's shining circle
The gems drop away!
When true hearts lie wither'd
And fond ones are flown,
Oh! who would inhabit
This bleak world alone?

The Jug of Punch

'Twas ve - ry ear - ly in the month of June As

I was sit - ting in my room A small bird sang on an

i - vy bush And the song she sang was the Jug of Punch. Too ral

loo-ral lay Too-ral loo-ral lay Too-ral loo-ral lay Too-ral

Irish Songs

loo - ral lay   A   small bird sang   on   an

i - vy bush and the   song she sang was the Jug of Punch.

Sign above a Dublin pub entrance

What more diversion can a man desire,
Than to be seated by a snug coal fire,
Upon his knee a pretty wench,
And on his table a jug of punch.
Too-ral loo-ral lay
Too-ral loo-ral lay
Too-ral loo-ral lay
Too-ral loo-ral lay
Upon his knee a pretty wench,
And on his table a jug of punch.

Now when I am dead and in my grave,
No costly tombstone will I crave
Just lay me down in my native heath
With a jug of punch at my head and my feet.
Too-ral loo-ral lay
Too-ral loo-ral lay
Too-ral loo-ral lay
Too-ral loo-ral lay
Just lay me down in my native heath
With a jug of punch at my head and feet.

'So fill to me the parting glass'

The Parting Glass

Oh,   all the mon-ey   e'er I had, I   spent it in   good

com-pa-ny, And   all the harm I've   ev-er done, a - las it was to

none but me, And   all   I've done for   want of   wit to

mem-'ry now   I   can't re - call; So   fill to me the

part - ing glass, Good_ night and joy__ be__ with you all.

Oh, all the comrades e'er I had,
They're sorry for my going away,
And all the sweethearts e'er I had,
They'd wished me one more day to stay.
But since it falls unto my lot
That I should rise and you should not,
I gently rise and softly call,
Goodnight and joy be with you all.

If I had money enough to spend,
And leisure time to sit awhile,
There is a fair maid in this town,
That sorely has my heart beguiled,
Her rosy cheeks and ruby lips,
I own, she has my heart in thrall,
Then fill to me the parting glass,
Goodnight and joy be with you all.

'Fill to me the parting glass' – Pub in Tralee, Co. Kerry

'As I roved out' – Inis Mór, Aran Islands

As I Roved Out

As I roved out on a May morn- ing, On a May morn-ing right ear - ly, I

met my love a - long the way, Oh__ Lord but she was ear - ly_____ And she sang

lilt a doo - dle lilt a doo - dle, lilt a doo - dle dee and she

hi - da-lan-da dee and she hi-da-lan-da-dee and she lan-day._____

Her boots were black and her stockings white,
And her buckles shone like silver,
And she had a dark and a rolling eye,
And her earrings tipped her shoulder.

Chorus

'What age are you, my nice sweet girl?
What age are you my honey?'
How modestly she answered me,
'I'll be sixteen age on Sunday.'

Chorus

I went to the house on the top of the hill
When the moon was shining clearly;
She arose to let me in,
For her mammy chanced to hear her.

Chorus

She caught her by the hair of her head,
And down to the room she brought her;
And with the root of a hazel twig,
She was the well-beat daughter.

Chorus

'Will you marry me now, my soldier lad?
Marry me now or never?
Will you marry me now, my soldier lad,
For you see I'm done forever?'

Chorus

'No, I won't marry you, my bonny wee girl,
I won't marry you, my honey,
For I have got a wife at home,
And how could I disown her?'

Chorus

A pint at night is my delight,
And a gallon in the morning;
The old women are my heartbreak,
But the young one is my darling.

Chorus

'Let us drink a health to the Holy Ground'

The Holy Ground

Fare - well my love-ly Di – nah, A thou-sand times A – dieu

__ For we're go-ing a - way from the Ho -ly Ground, And the girls we all loved

true____ We'll sail the South Seas ov – er and we'll re - turn for

sure_____ To see a - gain the girls we love and the Ho - ly Ground once

more_____ To the girl I do a - dore_____ And still I

live in hope to see the___ Ho - ly Ground once more_____

'The Holy Ground' – Clogher Head, Dingle Peninsula

Oh, the night was dark and stormy,
You scarce could see the moon,
And our good old ship was tossed about,
And her rigging all was torn:
With her seams agape and leaky,
With her timbers dozed and old,
And still I live in hopes to see,
The Holy Ground once more.
You're the girl I do adore
And still I live in hopes to see,
The Holy Ground once more.
Fine girl you are!

And now the storm is over,
And we are safe on shore,
Let us drink a health to the Holy Ground
And the girls that we adore;
We will drink strong ale and porter
Till we make the tap room roar
And when our money is spent
We will go to sea once more.
You're the girl I do adore
And still I live in hopes to see,
The Holy Ground once more.
Fine girl you are!

Dunmore Strand in Dingle Peninsula, Co. Kerry

The Kerry Dances

O the days of the Ker - ry dan - cing, O the days of the

pip - er's tune, O for one of those hours of glad - ness,

gone a - las like our youth too soon. When the boys be -

gan to gath - er in the glen of a sum - mer night, and the Ker - ry

pip-er's tun-ing, make us long with wild de-light,   O   to think of it,

O   to dream of   it,   fills   my heart   with   tears._____

Was there ever a sweeter colleen
In the dance than Eily More,
Or a prouder lad than Thady
As he boldly took the floor.
'Lads and lassies, to your places,
Up the middle and down again',
And the merry-hearted laughter
Ringing through the happy glen.
O to think of it, O to dream of it,
Fills my heart with tears.

O the days of the Kerry dancing,
O the ring of the piper's tune,
O for one of those hours of gladness,
Gone alas like our youth too soon.

Acknowledgements

page 4 © istockphoto.com/Judy Picciotto
page 6 © istockphoto.com/Christopher O'Driscoll
page 9 © istockphoto.com/Rolf Weschke
page 14 © Stockpix
page 16 © istockphoto.com/David Mathies
page 20 © Bill Holland
page 22 © istockphoto.com/Kerstin Bastian
page 26 © istockphoto.com/Robert Mayne
page 30 © istockphoto.com/Brian Kelly
page 32 © istockphoto.com/Mary Lee Woodward
page 34 © istockphoto.com/Steve Roche
page 36 © istockphoto.com/Miranda McMurray
page 38 © istockphoto.com/David Shawley
page 42 © istockphoto.com/Kelvin Wakefield
page 46 © istockphoto.com/Bernhard Weber
page 48 © istockphoto.com/rphotos
page 51 © istockphoto.com/Andrew Howe
page 54 © istockphoto.com/Ryan Ganley
page 60 © istockphoto.com/Tito Slack
page 63 © istockphoto.com/Boris Shapiro
page 64 © istockphoto.com/Diane Diederich
page 66 © istockphoto.com/cgnznt144
page 69 © istockphoto.com/Jane McIlroy
page 70 © istockphoto.com/Ciaran Walsh
page 74 © istockphoto.com/Alexander Tivanov
page 78 © istockphoto.com/Peter Bates
page 80 © istockphoto.com/Donall O'Cleirigh
page 83 © Stockpix
page 84 © istockphoto.com/Jonnie Morgan
page 88 © istockphoto.com/Donall O'Cleirigh
page 90 © istockphoto.com/Dan Carollo
page 92 © istockphoto.com/S. Greg Panosian

Index